10 Cut-Ups

by Bobby Lynn Maslen
pictures by John R. Maslen

Scholastic Inc.

New York • Toronto • London • Auckland • Sydney • Mexico City • New Delhi • Hong Kong • Buenos Aires

Numerals 1 - 10 for Book 9
Plural Endings - s

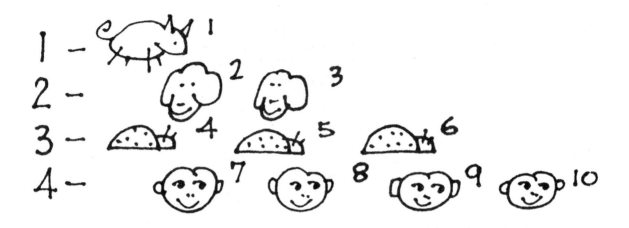

ISBN 0-545-02722-5

6 5 4 3 2   10 11/0

Printed in China   68
This edition first printing, September 2007

Jig has <u>1</u> wig.

1   2

<u>2</u> bugs in a rug.

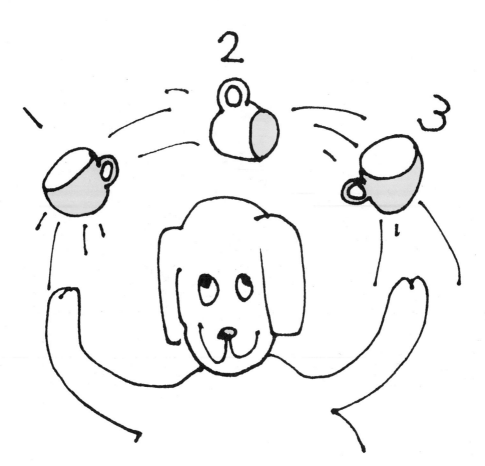

Pup has <u>3</u> cups.

Mac has <u>4</u> hats.

Dot has <u>5</u> pots.

Cat has <u>6</u> caps.

Ruff has <u>7</u> pups.

Mag has _8_ bags.
Muff has _9_ rags.

Dot has <u>10</u> ↰.

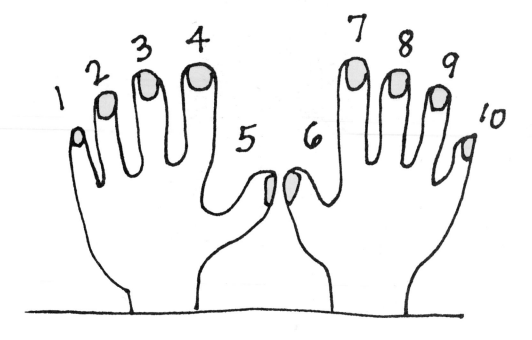

The End

Available Bob Books®:

Set 1: Beginning Readers — With consistent new sounds added gradually, your new reader is gently introduced to all the letters of the alphabet. They can soon say, "I read the whole book!®"

Set 2: Advancing Beginners — The use of three-letter words and consistent vowel sounds in slightly longer stories build skill and confidence.

Set 3: Word Families — Consonant blends, endings and a few sight words advance reading skills while the use of word families keep reading manageable.

Set 4: Complex Words — Longer books and complex words engage young readers as proficiency advances.

Set 5: Long Vowels — Silent *e* and other vowel blends build young readers' vocabulary and aptitude.

Bob Books® Collections:

Collection 1 — Includes Set 1: Beginning Readers and part of Set 2: Advancing Beginners

Collection 2 — Includes part of Set 2: Advancing Beginners and Set 3: Word Families

Collection 3 — Includes Set 4: Complex Words and Set 5: Long Vowels